THIS BOOK BELONGS TO:

_____

A

APPLE

B

BICYCLE

D

DINOSAUR

F

FISH

GIFT

H

HOUSE

I

ICE CREAM

JELLYFISH

M

MOON

N

NEST

O

OWL

P

PENCIL

QUEEN

R

RAINBOW

S

SUN

T

TRAIN

U

UNICORN

VIOLIN

WHALE

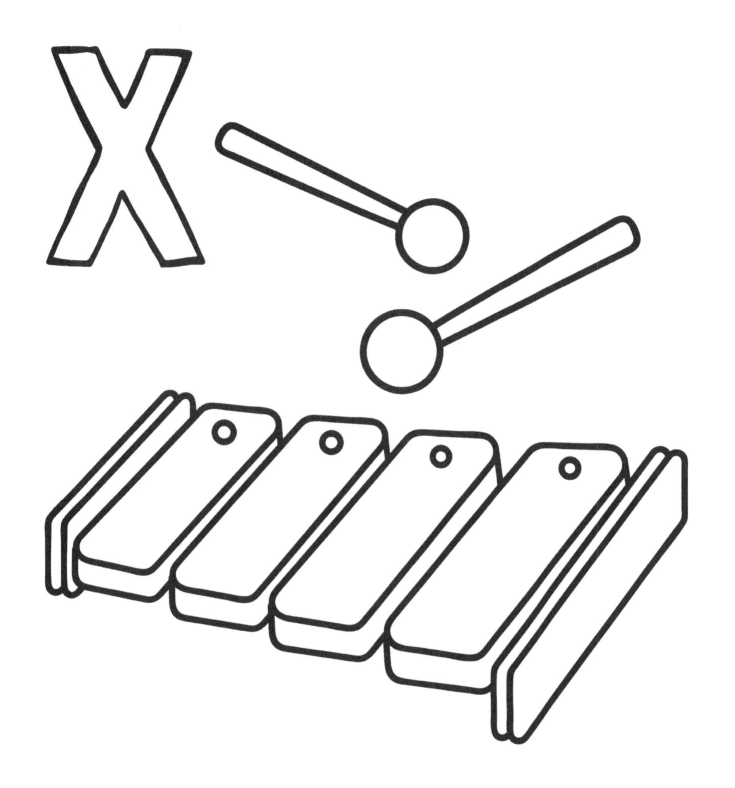

XYLOPHONE

Y

YOGURT

ZEBRA

1 2 3 4

5 6 7

8 9 10

NUMBERS

2

TWO

3

THREE

5

FIVE

6

SIX

SHAPES

TRIANGLE

SQUARE

RECTANGLE

CIRCLE

OVAL

COLORS

ORANGE

YELLOW

GREEN

BLUE

PURPLE

FEELINGS

SAD

SCARED

SURPRISED

CURIOUS

ANGRY

MEALS

BREAKFAST

LUNCH

DINNER

COLOR YOUR FAVORITE FRUITS

COLOR YOUR FAVORITE
VEGETABLES

GREETINGS

GOOD
AFTERNOON

GOOD
NIGHT

SEASONS

SPRING

FLOWERS

SUMMER

BEACH

FALL

LEAVES

WINTER

SNOW

MY TOWN

HOME

SCHOOL

LIBRARY

GROCERY STORE

PARK

FIRE STATION

RESTAURANT

Please consider leaving a review of our book on Amazon.
We'd appreciate it very much!

Thank you!
The happy crayons team

And if you're looking for more to color, please visit:
happycrayons.com

Made in the USA
Monee, IL
26 August 2022

12577563R10105